PROMPT ME

READING LOG & ANALYSIS

Prompt Me Series

BY
ROBIN WOODS

EPIC

Epic Books Publishing

www.epicbookspublishing.com

Lead Editor: Beth Braithwaite
Additional Editing: Brooke E. Wayne

You can write to info@RobinWoodsFiction.com

Cover Design created on Canva by Robin Woods
Wise Owl illustration is a public domain work
All stick figure illustrations drawn by Robin Woods

Fonts: Century, Calibri, Note This, and Sunday

Dedicated to M & A, You both make me so proud.
I love you the mostiest.

Special thanks to:
Tamar Hela for contributing content for foreshadowing and symbolism.
Brooke E. Wayne for helping me brainstorm and being a sounding board.
Beth Braithwaite for your encouragement and always making time for my scribbles.

Summary: A no-fuss way to log reading chapter-by-chapter and love the process.

[Reading log, Diary, Non-Fiction, Reference, Reading Workbook, Reading Journal]

ISBN-13: 978-1-941077-14-6
ISBN-10: 1-941077-14-5

TABLE OF CONTENTS

BOOKS ARE UNIQUELY PORTABLE MAGIC.

—STEPHEN KING

The wise owl would love to be colored.

INTRODUCTION

This year, I took on a new endeavor—homeschooling my two elementary kids after moving. My kids disliked answering lists of questions about literature. So, before they started hating books, I adapted something I had previously done with my high school and university students—even at that age, they still liked crayons. Breaking it down to the basics works well and spurs great discussion. My kids perform better going into discussion when they aren't taxed. This is how I solved that dilemma.

HOW TO USE THIS BOOK

This book is designed to be both flexible and fun. When you are reading, answering a bunch of questions isn't always exciting. So, this is a simple way to track what happens in a chapter without all the questions. In the lined portion, simply write down some bullet points about what happened. After, in the blank box, draw a picture of what you found to be the most powerful image in the chapter. This is flexible; if that doesn't work for you, then feel free to use it in a different way.

WHAT HAPPENED?

CHAPTER(S) 2	Starting page number 5
Make a bullet point list as you read.	Draw a picture of your favorite part.

- Wolf shows up again
- Pigs think they are safe because the house is made of sticks
- The wolf blows the house down.
- Pigs escape safely

RATING SYSTEM

After you read each book, you will have a chance to rate it.

Wow! This book was crazy good!	☆☆☆☆☆
I liked it a lot.	☆☆☆☆
I enjoyed most of it.	☆☆☆
I got through it. Not really my thing.	☆☆
I wouldn't recommend it—ever.	☆

HOW TO BREAKDOWN CHAPTERS

Every book has its own unique length. Some novels are long, others short. Each section has a different amount of spaces for chapters (ranging between 12-24). The number provided is noted at the top of each new book section and in the Table of Contents. You do not have to log your books in order—pick a section according to length. You can also log more than one chapter in a box (a little math is required). This number shows you how many sections there are for chapters.

BOOK ONE (12)

E.g. *If your book has 13 chapters, combine two chapters.*

Book Title ____
Author ____
□ Fiction □ Non-Fiction

LITERARY TERMS & DEVICES

Here are some definitions for common terms. Note: All terms given close-ups are noted with an *.

Allegory	A story or tale with two or more levels of meaning—a literal level and one or more symbolic levels. The events, setting, and characters in an allegory are symbols for ideas or qualities. *E.g. In* The Chronicles of Narnia, *Aslan represents a Christ-figure.*
Alliteration*	The repetition of consonant sounds at the beginning of words (see page 146).
Allusion	A reference to a well-known person, place, event, literary work, or work of art. Writers often make allusions to stories from the Bible, to Greek and Roman myths, to plays by Shakespeare, to political and historical events, and to other materials with which they can expect their readers to be familiar. *E.g. An adventure story that calls the villain a "big, bad wolf" is referring to* The Three Little Pigs. *Most people are familiar with that story, so you would know that the villain is probably going to be noisy about what he or she wants and "huff and puff."*
Characterization*	The act of creating and developing a character (see page 35).
Conflict*	A struggle between opposing forces (see page 49).
Dialogue	A conversation between characters. Each character has his or her own voice (personality), so each speaker sounds differently. So, a parent might use bigger words than a child or a person from Ireland would use different words than an American. *E.g. "Where do you think you're going, young miss?" asked her mother.* *"Outside," Mary replied, not wanting to be stopped.* *"Where's your jacket? It's raining buckets out there."* *"I want to get wet," Mary said, then ran out the door.*
Figurative Language	Writing or speech not meant to be taken literally. Writers use figurative language to express ideas in vivid and imaginative ways. *E.g. Jane jumped out of her skin when her brother scared her.* Jane didn't literally jump out of her skin, but she was genuinely scared.
Flashback*	An interruption in the story to give background from the past (see page 112).
Foreshadowing*	Clues that give us hints about future events (see page 22).
Hyperbole	Exaggeration for effect; not meant to be taken literally. *E.g. I have a million things to do today.*
Imagery	Descriptives used to create word pictures for the reader. The six senses are used to create these images (sight, sound, taste, touch, smell, or movement).

Irony	A difference between what is *said* and what is *meant*—or—between what is expected to happen and what actually happens. • In *verbal irony,* a word or a phrase is used to suggest the opposite of its usual meaning. *E.g. Fred says, "Wonderful!" when his car breaks down. He does not mean wonderful—he means terrible.* • In *dramatic irony,* there is a contradiction between what a character thinks and what the reader or the audience knows to be true. *E.g. Jane says, "I totally got an A on the assignment." But we know that her best friend, Kevin, took her paper and put his name on it.*
Metaphor*	A direct comparison of two unlike things (see page 80).
Juxtaposition*	Comparing and contrasting to make something clearer (see page 128).
Narrator	The character who tells the story. This person is not the author, but a creation of the author.
Onomatopoeia	Words that imitate the sound they represent. Often, the pronunciation suggests the meaning. *E.g. Buzz, tinkle, swish, kaboom, kapow, slurp, gurgle, sizzle, belch, etc.*
Personification	Giving animals, objects, or ideas characteristics only a human can have. It creates vivid imagery and interest while improving understanding. *E.g. The mountains frowned at us; the moon smiled down at the sailors; the car complained when she started it; the wind clawed at me; shy flowers peeked out; when the tree fell, the birds cried in sorrow; etc.*
Point of View*	The viewpoint or angle the author chooses to write the story (see page 64).
Prose	Ordinary writing—not poetry.
Setting	The physical place where the action of the story takes place, including location, time, and general environment.
Simile*	A comparison of two things using *like* or *as* (see page 80).
Subplot	A second storyline. It has its own characters and frequently a different theme than the main plot, usually having some relation to the main plot.
Symbolism*	Giving meaning to objects (see page 96).
Synonym	A word having the same or nearly the same meaning as another. *E.g. "Help" and "assist" or "hop" and "jump"*
Theme	The underlying message or "big idea" the author is trying to get across. *E.g. The theme of the* "Three Little Pigs" *is that it pays to do things right.*
Tone	The *feel* the author creates through word choice and world building.

BOOK ONE (14)

Book Title ____

Author ____

□ Fiction □ Non-Fiction

Draw your own cover for the book.

CHARACTERS

Create a character list for the book to help you keep things straight.

☐ List the characters as you read —or—

☐ Look up a list online and fill in the left column before reading

Character Name	Description (age, what they look like, etc.)

SETTING

Time Period	
Place	
Type of Environment	
Other Background Information	

WHAT HAPPENED?

CHAPTER(S) ________ Make a bullet point list as you read.	Starting page number ______ Draw a picture of your favorite part.
______ ______ ______ ______ ______ ______ ______	
CHAPTER(S) ________	Starting page number ______
______ ______ ______ ______ ______ ______ ______	

CHAPTER(S) ________ Make a bullet point list as you read.	Starting page number _______ Draw a picture of your favorite part.
______________________ ______________________ ______________________ ______________________ ______________________ ______________________ ______________________	

CHAPTER(S) ________	Starting page number _______
______________________ ______________________ ______________________ ______________________ ______________________ ______________________ ______________________	

CHAPTER(S) ________ Make a bullet point list as you read.	Starting page number ______ Draw a picture of your favorite part.
______________________________ ______________________________ ______________________________ ______________________________ ______________________________ ______________________________ ______________________________	
CHAPTER(S) ________	Starting page number ______
______________________________ ______________________________ ______________________________ ______________________________ ______________________________ ______________________________ ______________________________	

CHAPTER(S) ________ Make a bullet point list as you read.	Starting page number _______ Draw a picture of your favorite part.
______________________________ ______________________________ ______________________________ ______________________________ ______________________________ ______________________________ ______________________________	
CHAPTER(S) ________	**Starting page number _______**
______________________________ ______________________________ ______________________________ ______________________________ ______________________________ ______________________________ ______________________________	

CHAPTER(S) ________ Make a bullet point list as you read.	Starting page number ______ Draw a picture of your favorite part.
______ ______ ______ ______ ______ ______ ______	
CHAPTER(S) ________	Starting page number ______
______ ______ ______ ______ ______ ______ ______	

CHAPTER(S) ________ Make a bullet point list as you read.	Starting page number _______ Draw a picture of your favorite part.
___ ___ ___ ___ ___ ___ ___	

CHAPTER(S) ________	Starting page number _______
___ ___ ___ ___ ___ ___ ___	

CHAPTER(S) ________ Make a bullet point list as you read.	Starting page number ______ Draw a picture of your favorite part.
______________________________ ______________________________ ______________________________ ______________________________ ______________________________ ______________________________ ______________________________	
CHAPTER(S) ________	**Starting page number ______**
______________________________ ______________________________ ______________________________ ______________________________ ______________________________ ______________________________ ______________________________	

WHAT ABOUT IT?

My rating	☆☆☆☆☆
What was the theme (message)? What did the author want you to learn?	
What was your favorite part? Explain.	
Did you notice the author using any literary devices? (Literature terms)	
Would you change anything in the book?	
Other notes about the book.	

FORESHADOWING

The author is giving us hints and clues as to what is about to come. Usually foreshadowing happens at the beginning of a story or the beginning of a chapter so that readers can develop expectations for future events. The best type of foreshadowing is when a writer can be subtle and weave reminders throughout the story so that tension builds and what's coming becomes powerful.

Page content contributed by Tamar Hela

BOOK TWO (16)

Book Title ______________________________

Author ______________________________

□ Fiction □ Non-Fiction

Draw your own cover for the book.

CHARACTERS

Create a character list for the book to help you keep things straight.

☐ List the characters as you read —or—

☐ Look up a list online and fill in the left column before reading

Character Name	Description (age, what they look like, etc.)

SETTING

Time Period	
Place	
Type of Environment	
Other Background Information	

WHAT HAPPENED?

CHAPTER(S) ________ Make a bullet point list as you read.	Starting page number ______ Draw a picture of your favorite part.
______________________________ ______________________________ ______________________________ ______________________________ ______________________________ ______________________________ ______________________________	
CHAPTER(S) ________	Starting page number ______
______________________________ ______________________________ ______________________________ ______________________________ ______________________________ ______________________________ ______________________________	

CHAPTER(S) ________ Make a bullet point list as you read.	Starting page number _______ Draw a picture of your favorite part.
______________________________ ______________________________ ______________________________ ______________________________ ______________________________ ______________________________ ______________________________	
CHAPTER(S) ________	Starting page number _______
______________________________ ______________________________ ______________________________ ______________________________ ______________________________ ______________________________ ______________________________	

CHAPTER(S) ________ Make a bullet point list as you read.	Starting page number ______ Draw a picture of your favorite part.
____________________ ____________________ ____________________ ____________________ ____________________ ____________________ ____________________	

CHAPTER(S) ________	Starting page number ______
____________________ ____________________ ____________________ ____________________ ____________________ ____________________ ____________________	

CHAPTER(S) ________ Make a bullet point list as you read.	Starting page number ______ Draw a picture of your favorite part.
________________________ ________________________ ________________________ ________________________ ________________________ ________________________ ________________________	
CHAPTER(S) ________	Starting page number ______
________________________ ________________________ ________________________ ________________________ ________________________ ________________________ ________________________	

CHAPTER(S) ________ Make a bullet point list as you read.	Starting page number ______ Draw a picture of your favorite part.
____________________ ____________________ ____________________ ____________________ ____________________ ____________________ ____________________	
CHAPTER(S) ________	**Starting page number ______**
____________________ ____________________ ____________________ ____________________ ____________________ ____________________ ____________________	

CHAPTER(S) ________ Make a bullet point list as you read.	Starting page number _______ Draw a picture of your favorite part.
______________________________ ______________________________ ______________________________ ______________________________ ______________________________ ______________________________ ______________________________	
CHAPTER(S) ________	Starting page number _______
______________________________ ______________________________ ______________________________ ______________________________ ______________________________ ______________________________ ______________________________	

CHAPTER(S) ________ Make a bullet point list as you read.	Starting page number ______ Draw a picture of your favorite part.
______________________________ ______________________________ ______________________________ ______________________________ ______________________________ ______________________________ ______________________________	
CHAPTER(S) ________	Starting page number ______
______________________________ ______________________________ ______________________________ ______________________________ ______________________________ ______________________________ ______________________________	

CHAPTER(S) ________ Make a bullet point list as you read.	Starting page number ______ Draw a picture of your favorite part.
______________________________ ______________________________ ______________________________ ______________________________ ______________________________ ______________________________ ______________________________	
CHAPTER(S) ________	**Starting page number ______**
______________________________ ______________________________ ______________________________ ______________________________ ______________________________ ______________________________ ______________________________	

WHAT ABOUT IT?

My rating	☆ ☆ ☆ ☆ ☆
What was the theme (message)? What did the author want you to learn?	
What was your favorite part? Explain.	
Did you notice the author using any literary devices? (Literature terms)	
Would you change anything in the book?	
Other notes about the book.	

CHARACTERIZATION

Characterization is the way the author creates and develops a character. There are two primary methods—direct and indirect.

In *direct characterization,* a writer simply states a character's traits. The author might write something like this: She was quiet by nature, her eyes speaking more than her words. They were deep, blue like the sea on a stormy day.

In *indirect characterization*, the character is revealed by one of the following means:

- By the words, thoughts, or actions of the character
- By descriptions of the character's appearance or background
- By what other characters say about the character
- By the ways in which other characters react towards the character

Direct Characterization

The text states: Her hair moved like a waterfall, flowing in waves with each step.

Indirect Characterization

Other characters say things to or about the character, and we learn the same information.

BOOK THREE (16)

Book Title ______________________________________

Author ______________________________________

□ Fiction □ Non-Fiction

Draw your own cover for the book.

CHARACTERS

Create a character list for the book to help you keep things straight.

☐ List the characters as you read —or—

☐ Look up a list online and fill in the left column before reading

Character Name	Description (age, what they look like, etc.)

CHARACTERS CONTINUED

Character Name	Description (age, what they look like, etc.)

SETTING

Time Period	
Place	
Type of Environment	
Other Background Information	

WHAT HAPPENED?

CHAPTER(S) ________ Make a bullet point list as you read.	Starting page number ______ Draw a picture of your favorite part.
________________ ________________ ________________ ________________ ________________ ________________ ________________	
CHAPTER(S) ________	Starting page number ______
________________ ________________ ________________ ________________ ________________ ________________ ________________	

CHAPTER(S) ________ Make a bullet point list as you read.	Starting page number ______ Draw a picture of your favorite part.
____________________ ____________________ ____________________ ____________________ ____________________ ____________________ ____________________	

CHAPTER(S) ________	Starting page number ______
____________________ ____________________ ____________________ ____________________ ____________________ ____________________ ____________________	

CHAPTER(S) ________ Make a bullet point list as you read.	Starting page number ______ Draw a picture of your favorite part.

CHAPTER(S) ________	Starting page number ______

CHAPTER(S) ________ Make a bullet point list as you read.	Starting page number ______ Draw a picture of your favorite part.
______________________________ ______________________________ ______________________________ ______________________________ ______________________________ ______________________________ ______________________________	
CHAPTER(S) ________	Starting page number ______
______________________________ ______________________________ ______________________________ ______________________________ ______________________________ ______________________________ ______________________________	

CHAPTER(S) ________ Make a bullet point list as you read.	Starting page number ______ Draw a picture of your favorite part.
______________________________ ______________________________ ______________________________ ______________________________ ______________________________ ______________________________ ______________________________	

CHAPTER(S) ________	Starting page number ______
______________________________ ______________________________ ______________________________ ______________________________ ______________________________ ______________________________ ______________________________	

CHAPTER(S) ________ Make a bullet point list as you read.	Starting page number ______ Draw a picture of your favorite part.
______________________________ ______________________________ ______________________________ ______________________________ ______________________________ ______________________________ ______________________________	
CHAPTER(S) ________	Starting page number ______
______________________________ ______________________________ ______________________________ ______________________________ ______________________________ ______________________________ ______________________________	

CHAPTER(S) ________	Starting page number _______
Make a bullet point list as you read.	Draw a picture of your favorite part.

CHAPTER(S) ________	Starting page number _______

CHAPTER(S) ________ Make a bullet point list as you read.	Starting page number ______ Draw a picture of your favorite part.
______________________________ ______________________________ ______________________________ ______________________________ ______________________________ ______________________________ ______________________________	
CHAPTER(S) ________	Starting page number ______
______________________________ ______________________________ ______________________________ ______________________________ ______________________________ ______________________________ ______________________________	

WHAT ABOUT IT?

My rating	☆ ☆ ☆ ☆ ☆
What was the theme (message)? What did the author want you to learn?	
What was your favorite part? Explain.	
Did you notice the author using any literary devices? (Literature terms)	
Would you change anything in the book?	
Other notes about the book.	

CONFLICT

Good plots have conflict—this means two things are fighting against each another. There are five main types of conflict:

1. Struggle against another human or other humans
2. Internal struggle within the mind
3. Struggle against the forces of nature
4. Struggle against society
5. Struggle against the supernatural (God or fate)

Person versus Person

Person versus Self

Person versus Society

Person versus Nature

Person versus the Supernatural

(Bonus) Person versus Technology

BOOK FOUR (16)

Book Title ____

Author ____

□ Fiction □ Non-Fiction

Draw your own cover for the book.

CHARACTERS

Create a character list for the book to help you keep things straight.

☐ List the characters as you read —or—

☐ Look up a list online and fill in the left column before reading

Character Name	Description (age, what they look like, etc.)

CHARACTERS CONTINUED

Character Name	Description (age, what they look like, etc.)

SETTING

Time Period (When)	
Place (Where)	
Type of Environment	
Other Background Information	

WHAT HAPPENED?

CHAPTER(S) ________ Make a bullet point list as you read.	Starting page number _______ Draw a picture of your favorite part.
____________________ ____________________ ____________________ ____________________ ____________________ ____________________ ____________________	
CHAPTER(S) ________	Starting page number _______
____________________ ____________________ ____________________ ____________________ ____________________ ____________________ ____________________	

CHAPTER(S) ________ Make a bullet point list as you read.	Starting page number _______ Draw a picture of your favorite part.
______________________________ ______________________________ ______________________________ ______________________________ ______________________________ ______________________________ ______________________________	
CHAPTER(S) ________	**Starting page number** _______
______________________________ ______________________________ ______________________________ ______________________________ ______________________________ ______________________________ ______________________________	

CHAPTER(S) ________ Make a bullet point list as you read.	Starting page number _______ Draw a picture of your favorite part.

CHAPTER(S) ________	Starting page number _______

CHAPTER(S) ________ Make a bullet point list as you read.	Starting page number ______ Draw a picture of your favorite part.
CHAPTER(S) ________	Starting page number ______

CHAPTER(S) ________ Make a bullet point list as you read.	Starting page number _______ Draw a picture of your favorite part.
____________________ ____________________ ____________________ ____________________ ____________________ ____________________ ____________________	

CHAPTER(S) ________	Starting page number _______
____________________ ____________________ ____________________ ____________________ ____________________ ____________________ ____________________	

CHAPTER(S) ________ Make a bullet point list as you read.	Starting page number ______ Draw a picture of your favorite part.
____________________ ____________________ ____________________ ____________________ ____________________ ____________________ ____________________	
CHAPTER(S) ________	Starting page number ______
____________________ ____________________ ____________________ ____________________ ____________________ ____________________ ____________________	

CHAPTER(S) ________ Make a bullet point list as you read.	Starting page number _______ Draw a picture of your favorite part.
______________________________ ______________________________ ______________________________ ______________________________ ______________________________ ______________________________ ______________________________	
CHAPTER(S) ________	Starting page number _______
______________________________ ______________________________ ______________________________ ______________________________ ______________________________ ______________________________ ______________________________	

CHAPTER(S) ________ Make a bullet point list as you read.	Starting page number _______ Draw a picture of your favorite part.
________________________________ ________________________________ ________________________________ ________________________________ ________________________________ ________________________________ ________________________________	

CHAPTER(S) ________	Starting page number _______
________________________________ ________________________________ ________________________________ ________________________________ ________________________________ ________________________________ ________________________________	

CHAPTER(S) ________ Make a bullet point list as you read.	Starting page number _______ Draw a picture of your favorite part.
____________________ ____________________ ____________________ ____________________ ____________________ ____________________ ____________________	
CHAPTER(S) ________	Starting page number _______
____________________ ____________________ ____________________ ____________________ ____________________ ____________________ ____________________	

WHAT ABOUT IT?

My rating	☆ ☆ ☆ ☆ ☆
What was the theme (message)? What did the author want you to learn?	
What was your favorite part? Explain.	
Did you notice the author using any literary devices? (Literature terms)	
Would you change anything in the book?	
Other notes about the book.	

POINT OF VIEW

The viewpoint from which the author tells his or her story. The three main ones are:

Omniscient: the narrator knows all. We can see into different characters' minds and see events that are happening at the exact same time in different parts of the world. Pronouns used: he, she, it, they, him, her, them, his, her, hers, its, their, and theirs.

First Person: the narrator tells the story as he or she experiences it or sees it. E.g. Defoe's *Robinson Crusoe*. Pronouns used: I, me, mine, ours, and we.

Third Person: a character *in* the story is narrating as he or she participates. This point of view is limited to one character. This character can be major or minor. Once in a while, the author will alternate between two characters narrating, but it is always limited to one character at a time. Pronouns used: he, she, it, they, him, her, them, his, her, hers, its, their, and theirs.

BOOK FIVE (20)

Book Title ______________________________

Author ______________________________

□ Fiction □ Non-Fiction

Draw your own cover for the book.

CHARACTERS

Create a character list for the book to help you keep things straight.

☐ List the characters as you read —or—

☐ Look up a list online and fill in the left column before reading

Character Name	Description (age, what they look like, etc.)

CHARACTERS CONTINUED

Character Name	Description (age, what they look like, etc.)

SETTING

Time Period (When)	
Place (Where)	
Type of Environment	
Other Background Information	

WHAT HAPPENED?

CHAPTER(S) ________ Make a bullet point list as you read.	Starting page number _______ Draw a picture of your favorite part.
______________________________ ______________________________ ______________________________ ______________________________ ______________________________ ______________________________ ______________________________	
CHAPTER(S) ________	Starting page number _______
______________________________ ______________________________ ______________________________ ______________________________ ______________________________ ______________________________ ______________________________	

CHAPTER(S) ________ Make a bullet point list as you read.	Starting page number ______ Draw a picture of your favorite part.
______________________ ______________________ ______________________ ______________________ ______________________ ______________________ ______________________	

CHAPTER(S) ________	Starting page number ______
______________________ ______________________ ______________________ ______________________ ______________________ ______________________ ______________________	

CHAPTER(S) ________ Make a bullet point list as you read.	Starting page number _______ Draw a picture of your favorite part.
________________________________ ________________________________ ________________________________ ________________________________ ________________________________ ________________________________ ________________________________	
CHAPTER(S) ________	Starting page number _______
________________________________ ________________________________ ________________________________ ________________________________ ________________________________ ________________________________ ________________________________	

CHAPTER(S) ________ Make a bullet point list as you read.	Starting page number ______ Draw a picture of your favorite part.
______________________________ ______________________________ ______________________________ ______________________________ ______________________________ ______________________________ ______________________________	
CHAPTER(S) ________	Starting page number ______
______________________________ ______________________________ ______________________________ ______________________________ ______________________________ ______________________________ ______________________________	

CHAPTER(S) ________ Make a bullet point list as you read.	Starting page number _______ Draw a picture of your favorite part.
______________________________ ______________________________ ______________________________ ______________________________ ______________________________ ______________________________ ______________________________	
CHAPTER(S) ________	Starting page number _______
______________________________ ______________________________ ______________________________ ______________________________ ______________________________ ______________________________ ______________________________	

CHAPTER(S) ________ Make a bullet point list as you read.	Starting page number ______ Draw a picture of your favorite part.
______________________________ ______________________________ ______________________________ ______________________________ ______________________________ ______________________________ ______________________________	

CHAPTER(S) ________	Starting page number ______
______________________________ ______________________________ ______________________________ ______________________________ ______________________________ ______________________________ ______________________________	

CHAPTER(S) ________ Make a bullet point list as you read.	Starting page number _______ Draw a picture of your favorite part.
______________________________ ______________________________ ______________________________ ______________________________ ______________________________ ______________________________ ______________________________	
CHAPTER(S) ________	**Starting page number _______**
______________________________ ______________________________ ______________________________ ______________________________ ______________________________ ______________________________ ______________________________	

CHAPTER(S) ________ Make a bullet point list as you read.	Starting page number _______ Draw a picture of your favorite part.
______________________________ ______________________________ ______________________________ ______________________________ ______________________________ ______________________________ ______________________________	

CHAPTER(S) ________	Starting page number _______
______________________________ ______________________________ ______________________________ ______________________________ ______________________________ ______________________________ ______________________________	

CHAPTER(S) ________ Make a bullet point list as you read.	Starting page number ______ Draw a picture of your favorite part.
______________________________ ______________________________ ______________________________ ______________________________ ______________________________ ______________________________ ______________________________	
CHAPTER(S) ________	Starting page number ______
______________________________ ______________________________ ______________________________ ______________________________ ______________________________ ______________________________ ______________________________	

CHAPTER(S) ________ Make a bullet point list as you read.	Starting page number ______ Draw a picture of your favorite part.
____________________ ____________________ ____________________ ____________________ ____________________ ____________________ ____________________	
CHAPTER(S) ________	Starting page number ______
____________________ ____________________ ____________________ ____________________ ____________________ ____________________ ____________________	

WHAT ABOUT IT?

My rating	☆ ☆ ☆ ☆ ☆
What was the theme (message)? What did the author want you to learn?	
What was your favorite part? Explain.	
Did you notice the author using any literary devices? (Literature terms)	
Would you change anything in the book?	
Other notes about the book.	

METAPHOR & SIMILE

Definition & Purpose

Metaphor

It is designed to create a vivid image to explain a topic or idea and give the reader understanding. The comparison always swaps one subject with another.

E.g. Fred = angel.

Simile

It is designed to create a picture *and* provide an example. The comparison *always* uses "like" or "as." This is the easiest way to tell a metaphor and simile apart.

Examples

Fred is an angel.

Fred was a pig at lunch.

The car was an oven.

You are my sunshine.

Fred is *as* innocent as an angel

Fred ate *like* a pig at lunch.

The car was *as* hot as an oven.

You are *like* my own personal sun.

METAPHOR

Direct comparison

SIMILE

Comparison using like or as

BOOK SIX (20)

Book Title ______________________________

Author ______________________________

□ Fiction □ Non-Fiction

Draw your own cover for the book.

CHARACTERS

Create a character list for the book to help you keep things straight.

☐ List the characters as you read —or—

☐ Look up a list online and fill in the left column before reading

Character Name	Description (age, what they look like, etc.)

CHARACTERS CONTINUED

Character Name	Description (age, what they look like, etc.)

SETTING

Time Period (When)	
Place (Where)	
Type of Environment	
Other Background Information	

WHAT HAPPENED?

CHAPTER(S) ________ Make a bullet point list as you read.	Starting page number ______ Draw a picture of your favorite part.
______________________________ ______________________________ ______________________________ ______________________________ ______________________________ ______________________________ ______________________________	
CHAPTER(S) ________	Starting page number ______
______________________________ ______________________________ ______________________________ ______________________________ ______________________________ ______________________________ ______________________________	

CHAPTER(S) ________ Make a bullet point list as you read.	Starting page number _______ Draw a picture of your favorite part.
________________________________ ________________________________ ________________________________ ________________________________ ________________________________ ________________________________ ________________________________	
CHAPTER(S) ________	Starting page number _______
________________________________ ________________________________ ________________________________ ________________________________ ________________________________ ________________________________ ________________________________	

CHAPTER(S) ________ Make a bullet point list as you read.	Starting page number _______ Draw a picture of your favorite part.
______________________________ ______________________________ ______________________________ ______________________________ ______________________________ ______________________________ ______________________________	
CHAPTER(S) ________	Starting page number _______
______________________________ ______________________________ ______________________________ ______________________________ ______________________________ ______________________________ ______________________________	

CHAPTER(S) ________ Make a bullet point list as you read.	Starting page number _______ Draw a picture of your favorite part.
________________________________ ________________________________ ________________________________ ________________________________ ________________________________ ________________________________ ________________________________	

CHAPTER(S) ________	Starting page number _______
________________________________ ________________________________ ________________________________ ________________________________ ________________________________ ________________________________ ________________________________	

CHAPTER(S) ________ Make a bullet point list as you read.	Starting page number _______ Draw a picture of your favorite part.
CHAPTER(S) ________	Starting page number _______

CHAPTER(S) ________ Make a bullet point list as you read.	Starting page number _______ Draw a picture of your favorite part.
___ ___ ___ ___ ___ ___ ___	
CHAPTER(S) ________	Starting page number _______
___ ___ ___ ___ ___ ___ ___	

CHAPTER(S) ________ Make a bullet point list as you read.	Starting page number ______ Draw a picture of your favorite part.
________ ________ ________ ________ ________ ________ ________	

CHAPTER(S) ________	Starting page number ______
________ ________ ________ ________ ________ ________ ________	

CHAPTER(S) ________ Make a bullet point list as you read.	Starting page number ______ Draw a picture of your favorite part.

CHAPTER(S) ________	Starting page number ______

CHAPTER(S) ________ Make a bullet point list as you read.	Starting page number _______ Draw a picture of your favorite part.
______________________________ ______________________________ ______________________________ ______________________________ ______________________________ ______________________________ ______________________________	
CHAPTER(S) ________	**Starting page number _______**
______________________________ ______________________________ ______________________________ ______________________________ ______________________________ ______________________________ ______________________________	

CHAPTER(S) ________ Make a bullet point list as you read.	Starting page number ______ Draw a picture of your favorite part.
______________________________ ______________________________ ______________________________ ______________________________ ______________________________ ______________________________ ______________________________	
CHAPTER(S) ________	Starting page number ______
______________________________ ______________________________ ______________________________ ______________________________ ______________________________ ______________________________ ______________________________	

WHAT ABOUT IT?

My rating	☆ ☆ ☆ ☆ ☆
What was the theme (message)? What did the author want you to learn?	
What was your favorite part? Explain.	
Did you notice the author using any literary devices? (Literature terms)	
Would you change anything in the book?	
Other notes about the book.	

SYMBOLISM

The author gives meaning to objects that stand for or represent something else. Symbolism can play a role in fiction writing by creating more complexity and meaning in the story. Even every day objects can become symbols, creating a poetic twist without a writer stating the obvious.

Some symbols mean the same thing all over the world.
E.g. the cross representing Christ's death, the ocean representing eternity and time, and a long trip representing the journey through life.

Other symbols only have meaning within the context of one author's work.
E.g. In Beauty & the Beast, *the rose represents passing time.*

Sometimes the characters themselves can become a symbol.
E.g. Pinocchio represents those who lie, Chicken Little symbolizes alarmists, and Peter Pan is symbolic of someone who doesn't want to grow up.

Page content contributed by Tamar Hela

BOOK SEVEN (20)

Book Title ______________________________

Author ______________________________

□ Fiction □ Non-Fiction

Draw your own cover for the book.

CHARACTERS

Create a character list for the book to help you keep things straight.

☐ List the characters as you read —or—

☐ Look up a list online and fill in the left column before reading

Character Name	Description (age, what they look like, etc.)

CHARACTERS CONTINUED

Character Name	Description (age, what they look like, etc.)

SETTING

Time Period (When)	
Place (Where)	
Type of Environment	
Other Background Information	

WHAT HAPPENED?

CHAPTER(S) ________ Make a bullet point list as you read.	Starting page number ______ Draw a picture of your favorite part.
______________________________ ______________________________ ______________________________ ______________________________ ______________________________ ______________________________ ______________________________	
CHAPTER(S) ________	Starting page number ______
______________________________ ______________________________ ______________________________ ______________________________ ______________________________ ______________________________ ______________________________	

CHAPTER(S) ________ Make a bullet point list as you read.	Starting page number ______ Draw a picture of your favorite part.
______________________________ ______________________________ ______________________________ ______________________________ ______________________________ ______________________________ ______________________________	
CHAPTER(S) ________	Starting page number ______
______________________________ ______________________________ ______________________________ ______________________________ ______________________________ ______________________________ ______________________________	

CHAPTER(S) ________ Make a bullet point list as you read.	Starting page number ______ Draw a picture of your favorite part.
______________________________ ______________________________ ______________________________ ______________________________ ______________________________ ______________________________ ______________________________	
CHAPTER(S) ________	Starting page number ______
______________________________ ______________________________ ______________________________ ______________________________ ______________________________ ______________________________ ______________________________	

CHAPTER(S) ________ Make a bullet point list as you read.	Starting page number ______ Draw a picture of your favorite part.
______________________________ ______________________________ ______________________________ ______________________________ ______________________________ ______________________________ ______________________________	
CHAPTER(S) ________	Starting page number ______
______________________________ ______________________________ ______________________________ ______________________________ ______________________________ ______________________________ ______________________________	

CHAPTER(S) ________ Make a bullet point list as you read.	Starting page number ______ Draw a picture of your favorite part.
CHAPTER(S) ________	Starting page number ______

CHAPTER(S) ________ Make a bullet point list as you read.	Starting page number ______ Draw a picture of your favorite part.

CHAPTER(S) ________	Starting page number ______

CHAPTER(S) ________ Make a bullet point list as you read.	Starting page number _______ Draw a picture of your favorite part.
______________________________ ______________________________ ______________________________ ______________________________ ______________________________ ______________________________ ______________________________	
CHAPTER(S) ________	Starting page number _______
______________________________ ______________________________ ______________________________ ______________________________ ______________________________ ______________________________ ______________________________	

CHAPTER(S) ________	Starting page number _______
Make a bullet point list as you read.	Draw a picture of your favorite part.
______________________________ ______________________________ ______________________________ ______________________________ ______________________________ ______________________________ ______________________________	

CHAPTER(S) ________	Starting page number _______
______________________________ ______________________________ ______________________________ ______________________________ ______________________________ ______________________________ ______________________________	

CHAPTER(S) ________ Make a bullet point list as you read.	Starting page number ______ Draw a picture of your favorite part.
CHAPTER(S) ________	Starting page number ______

CHAPTER(S) ________ Make a bullet point list as you read.	Starting page number ______ Draw a picture of your favorite part.
______________________________ ______________________________ ______________________________ ______________________________ ______________________________ ______________________________ ______________________________	
CHAPTER(S) ________	**Starting page number ______**
______________________________ ______________________________ ______________________________ ______________________________ ______________________________ ______________________________ ______________________________	

WHAT ABOUT IT?

My rating	☆ ☆ ☆ ☆ ☆
What was the theme (message)? What did the author want you to learn?	
What was your favorite part? Explain.	
Did you notice the author using any literary devices? (Literature terms)	
Would you change anything in the book?	
Other notes about the book.	

FLASHBACKS

A flashback is a break in a story that describes events that have already occurred in the past. This device is often used to give the reader more information or details about backgrounds, characters, events, setting, plot, and the like.

In other words, it moves the reader from the present order of events, to past events to show the reader something important.

E.g. Fred is afraid of heights and won't look into a canyon. A flashback can show us that his fear comes from falling off the monkey bars when he was a child.

LINEAR & NON-LINEAR TIMELINES

Don't be intimidated by the fancy sounding words. Linear may sound hard, but it really isn't. The root is LINE, and you know what a straight line is. Right? A linear story is simply a story told in a straight line—it has a beginning, middle, and end. It never stops and gives you a story from the past. So, a non-linear story does not go in a straight line. This type of story uses flashbacks or flash forwards.

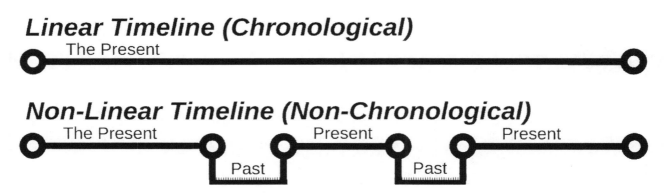

Linear Timeline (Chronological)

Non-Linear Timeline (Non-Chronological)

BOOK EIGHT (20)

Book Title ______________________________

Author ______________________________

□ Fiction □ Non-Fiction

Draw your own cover for the book.

CHARACTERS

Create a character list for the book to help you keep things straight.

☐ List the characters as you read —or—

☐ Look up a list online and fill in the left column before reading

Character Name	Description (age, what they look like, etc.)

CHARACTERS CONTINUED

Character Name	Description (age, what they look like, etc.)

SETTING

Time Period (When)	
Place (Where)	
Type of Environment	
Other Background Information	

WHAT HAPPENED?

CHAPTER(S) ________ Make a bullet point list as you read.	Starting page number ______ Draw a picture of your favorite part.
______________________________ ______________________________ ______________________________ ______________________________ ______________________________ ______________________________ ______________________________	
CHAPTER(S) ________	Starting page number ______
______________________________ ______________________________ ______________________________ ______________________________ ______________________________ ______________________________ ______________________________	

CHAPTER(S) ________ Make a bullet point list as you read.	Starting page number _______ Draw a picture of your favorite part.
______________________________ ______________________________ ______________________________ ______________________________ ______________________________ ______________________________ ______________________________	
CHAPTER(S) ________	Starting page number _______
______________________________ ______________________________ ______________________________ ______________________________ ______________________________ ______________________________ ______________________________	

CHAPTER(S) ________ Make a bullet point list as you read.	Starting page number ______ Draw a picture of your favorite part.
______________________________ ______________________________ ______________________________ ______________________________ ______________________________ ______________________________ ______________________________	
CHAPTER(S) ________	**Starting page number ______**
______________________________ ______________________________ ______________________________ ______________________________ ______________________________ ______________________________ ______________________________	

<table>
<tr><td>CHAPTER(S) ________

Make a bullet point list as you read.</td><td>Starting page number ______

Draw a picture of your favorite part.</td></tr>
<tr><td>______________________________
____
____
____
____
____
______________________________</td><td></td></tr>
<tr><td>CHAPTER(S) ________</td><td>Starting page number ______</td></tr>
<tr><td>______________________________
____
____
____
____
____
______________________________</td><td></td></tr>
</table>

CHAPTER(S) ________ Make a bullet point list as you read.	Starting page number _______ Draw a picture of your favorite part.
CHAPTER(S) ________	Starting page number _______

CHAPTER(S) ________ Make a bullet point list as you read.	Starting page number ______ Draw a picture of your favorite part.
________________________________ ________________________________ ________________________________ ________________________________ ________________________________ ________________________________ ________________________________	
CHAPTER(S) ________	Starting page number ______
________________________________ ________________________________ ________________________________ ________________________________ ________________________________ ________________________________ ________________________________	

CHAPTER(S) ________ Make a bullet point list as you read.	Starting page number _______ Draw a picture of your favorite part.
______________________________ ______________________________ ______________________________ ______________________________ ______________________________ ______________________________ ______________________________	
CHAPTER(S) ________	Starting page number _______
______________________________ ______________________________ ______________________________ ______________________________ ______________________________ ______________________________ ______________________________	

CHAPTER(S) ________ Make a bullet point list as you read.	Starting page number _______ Draw a picture of your favorite part.
______________________________ ______________________________ ______________________________ ______________________________ ______________________________ ______________________________ ______________________________	
CHAPTER(S) ________	Starting page number _______
______________________________ ______________________________ ______________________________ ______________________________ ______________________________ ______________________________ ______________________________	

CHAPTER(S) ________ Make a bullet point list as you read.	Starting page number ______ Draw a picture of your favorite part.
________________ ________________ ________________ ________________ ________________ ________________ ________________	

CHAPTER(S) ________	Starting page number ______
________________ ________________ ________________ ________________ ________________ ________________ ________________	

CHAPTER(S) ________ Make a bullet point list as you read.	Starting page number _______ Draw a picture of your favorite part.
________________________________ ________________________________ ________________________________ ________________________________ ________________________________ ________________________________ ________________________________	
CHAPTER(S) ________	Starting page number _______
________________________________ ________________________________ ________________________________ ________________________________ ________________________________ ________________________________ ________________________________	

WHAT ABOUT IT?

My rating	☆ ☆ ☆ ☆ ☆
What was the theme (message)? What did the author want you to learn?	
What was your favorite part? Explain.	
Did you notice the author using any literary devices? (Literature terms)	
Would you change anything in the book?	
Other notes about the book.	

JUXTAPOSITION

The comparing and contrasting of two or more different ideas or objects. This literary device is often used to help create a clearer picture of the characteristics of one object or idea by comparing it with those of another.

E.g. One of the most famous literary examples of juxtaposition is the opening passage from Charles Dickens' novel, *A Tale of Two Cities*:

"It was the best of times, it was the worst of times,
it was the age of wisdom, it was the age of foolishness, ...
it was the season of Light, it was the season of Darkness,
it was the spring of hope, it was the winter of despair ..."

From this passage we can see that a confusing time filled with extreme differences.

E.g. Another famous example of juxtaposition is the devil versus angel comparison. When we see the characters together, we can see just how different each character is.

BOOK NINE (24)

Book Title ______________________________

Author ______________________________

☐ Fiction ☐ Non-Fiction

Draw your own cover for the book.

CHARACTERS

Create a character list for the book to help you keep things straight.

☐ List the characters as you read —or—

☐ Look up a list online and fill in the left column before reading

Character Name	Description (age, what they look like, etc.)

CHARACTERS CONTINUED

Character Name	Description (age, what they look like, etc.)

SETTING

Time Period (When)	
Place (Where)	
Type of Environment	
Other Background Information	

WHAT HAPPENED?

CHAPTER(S) ________ Make a bullet point list as you read.	Starting page number _______ Draw a picture of your favorite part.
___ ___ ___ ___ ___ ___ ___	
CHAPTER(S) ________	Starting page number _______
___ ___ ___ ___ ___ ___ ___	

CHAPTER(S) ________ Make a bullet point list as you read.	Starting page number _______ Draw a picture of your favorite part.
______________________________ ______________________________ ______________________________ ______________________________ ______________________________ ______________________________ ______________________________	
CHAPTER(S) ________	Starting page number _______
______________________________ ______________________________ ______________________________ ______________________________ ______________________________ ______________________________ ______________________________	

CHAPTER(S) ________ Make a bullet point list as you read.	Starting page number _______ Draw a picture of your favorite part.
______________________________ ______________________________ ______________________________ ______________________________ ______________________________ ______________________________ ______________________________	
CHAPTER(S) ________	Starting page number _______
______________________________ ______________________________ ______________________________ ______________________________ ______________________________ ______________________________ ______________________________ ______________________________	

CHAPTER(S) ________ Make a bullet point list as you read.	Starting page number ______ Draw a picture of your favorite part.
______________________________ ______________________________ ______________________________ ______________________________ ______________________________ ______________________________ ______________________________	
CHAPTER(S) ________	Starting page number ______
______________________________ ______________________________ ______________________________ ______________________________ ______________________________ ______________________________ ______________________________	

CHAPTER(S) ________	Starting page number _______
Make a bullet point list as you read.	Draw a picture of your favorite part.
______________________________	
______________________________	
______________________________	
______________________________	
______________________________	
______________________________	
______________________________	
CHAPTER(S) ________	**Starting page number _______**
______________________________	
______________________________	
______________________________	
______________________________	
______________________________	
______________________________	
______________________________	

CHAPTER(S) ________ Make a bullet point list as you read.	Starting page number ______ Draw a picture of your favorite part.
______________________________ ______________________________ ______________________________ ______________________________ ______________________________ ______________________________ ______________________________	
CHAPTER(S) ________	Starting page number ______
______________________________ ______________________________ ______________________________ ______________________________ ______________________________ ______________________________ ______________________________	

CHAPTER(S) ________ Make a bullet point list as you read.	Starting page number _______ Draw a picture of your favorite part.
______________________________ ______________________________ ______________________________ ______________________________ ______________________________ ______________________________ ______________________________	
CHAPTER(S) ________	Starting page number _______
______________________________ ______________________________ ______________________________ ______________________________ ______________________________ ______________________________ ______________________________	

CHAPTER(S) ________ Make a bullet point list as you read.	Starting page number _______ Draw a picture of your favorite part.
________________ ________________ ________________ ________________ ________________ ________________ ________________	
CHAPTER(S) ________	Starting page number _______
________________ ________________ ________________ ________________ ________________ ________________ ________________	

CHAPTER(S) ________ Make a bullet point list as you read.	Starting page number ______ Draw a picture of your favorite part.
______________________________ ______________________________ ______________________________ ______________________________ ______________________________ ______________________________ ______________________________	
CHAPTER(S) ________	Starting page number ______
______________________________ ______________________________ ______________________________ ______________________________ ______________________________ ______________________________ ______________________________	

CHAPTER(S) ________ Make a bullet point list as you read.	Starting page number ______ Draw a picture of your favorite part.
______________________________ ______________________________ ______________________________ ______________________________ ______________________________ ______________________________ ______________________________	
CHAPTER(S) ________	Starting page number ______
______________________________ ______________________________ ______________________________ ______________________________ ______________________________ ______________________________ ______________________________	

CHAPTER(S) ________ Make a bullet point list as you read.	Starting page number _______ Draw a picture of your favorite part.
______________________________ ______________________________ ______________________________ ______________________________ ______________________________ ______________________________ ______________________________	
CHAPTER(S) ________	Starting page number _______
______________________________ ______________________________ ______________________________ ______________________________ ______________________________ ______________________________ ______________________________	

CHAPTER(S) ________	Starting page number _______
Make a bullet point list as you read.	Draw a picture of your favorite part.

CHAPTER(S) ________	Starting page number _______

WHAT ABOUT IT?

My rating	☆ ☆ ☆ ☆ ☆
What was the theme (message)? What did the author want you to learn?	
What was your favorite part? Explain.	
Did you notice the author using any literary devices? (Literature terms)	
Would you change anything in the book?	
Other notes about the book.	

ALLITERATION

The repetition of consonant sounds at the beginning of words. Such as…

- **S**he **s**ells **s**eashells by the **s**eashore.
- A **b**ig **b**lack **b**ug **b**it a **b**ig **b**lack **b**ear.
- **G**reen **g**lass **g**lobes **g**low **g**reenly.
- **W**hich **w**itch **s**witched the **S**wiss wristwatches?

Underline the alliteration in the following phrases.

- Frivolously fanciful Fannie fried fresh fish furiously.
- Seven silly seven-year-olds singing super loud.
- How much wood would a woodchuck chuck if a woodchuck could chuck wood?
- Peter Piper picked a peck of pickled peppers. How many pickled peppers did Peter Piper pick?

Write a few phrases using alliteration.

Give papa a cup of proper coffee in a copper coffee cup.

BOOK TEN (24)

Book Title ____

Author ____

□ Fiction □ Non-Fiction

Draw your own cover for the book.

CHARACTERS

Create a character list for the book to help you keep things straight.

☐ List the characters as you read —or—

☐ Look up a list online and fill in the left column before reading

Character Name	Description (age, what they look like, etc.)

CHARACTERS CONTINUED

Character Name	Description (age, what they look like, etc.)

SETTING

Time Period (When)	
Place (Where)	
Type of Environment	
Other Background Information	

WHAT HAPPENED?

CHAPTER(S) ________ Make a bullet point list as you read.	Starting page number ______ Draw a picture of your favorite part.
______________________________ ______________________________ ______________________________ ______________________________ ______________________________ ______________________________ ______________________________	
CHAPTER(S) ________	Starting page number ______
______________________________ ______________________________ ______________________________ ______________________________ ______________________________ ______________________________ ______________________________	

CHAPTER(S) ________ Make a bullet point list as you read.	Starting page number _______ Draw a picture of your favorite part.
____________________ ____________________ ____________________ ____________________ ____________________ ____________________ ____________________	
CHAPTER(S) ________	Starting page number _______
____________________ ____________________ ____________________ ____________________ ____________________ ____________________ ____________________	

CHAPTER(S) ________ Make a bullet point list as you read.	Starting page number _______ Draw a picture of your favorite part.
______________________________ ______________________________ ______________________________ ______________________________ ______________________________ ______________________________ ______________________________	
CHAPTER(S) ________	Starting page number _______
______________________________ ______________________________ ______________________________ ______________________________ ______________________________ ______________________________ ______________________________ ______________________________	

CHAPTER(S) ________ Make a bullet point list as you read.	Starting page number ______ Draw a picture of your favorite part.
____________________ ____________________ ____________________ ____________________ ____________________ ____________________ ____________________	
CHAPTER(S) ________	Starting page number ______
____________________ ____________________ ____________________ ____________________ ____________________ ____________________ ____________________	

CHAPTER(S) ________ Make a bullet point list as you read.	Starting page number ______ Draw a picture of your favorite part.
____________________ ____________________ ____________________ ____________________ ____________________ ____________________ ____________________	

CHAPTER(S) ________	Starting page number ______
____________________ ____________________ ____________________ ____________________ ____________________ ____________________ ____________________	

CHAPTER(S) _______ Make a bullet point list as you read.	Starting page number ______ Draw a picture of your favorite part.

CHAPTER(S) _______	Starting page number ______

CHAPTER(S) ________ Make a bullet point list as you read.	Starting page number _______ Draw a picture of your favorite part.
________________________________ ________________________________ ________________________________ ________________________________ ________________________________ ________________________________ ________________________________	
CHAPTER(S) ________	Starting page number _______
________________________________ ________________________________ ________________________________ ________________________________ ________________________________ ________________________________ ________________________________	

CHAPTER(S) ________ Make a bullet point list as you read.	Starting page number ______ Draw a picture of your favorite part.
______________________________ ______________________________ ______________________________ ______________________________ ______________________________ ______________________________ ______________________________	
CHAPTER(S) ________	Starting page number ______
______________________________ ______________________________ ______________________________ ______________________________ ______________________________ ______________________________ ______________________________	

CHAPTER(S) ________ Make a bullet point list as you read.	Starting page number _______ Draw a picture of your favorite part.
______________________________ ______________________________ ______________________________ ______________________________ ______________________________ ______________________________ ______________________________	
CHAPTER(S) ________	Starting page number _______
______________________________ ______________________________ ______________________________ ______________________________ ______________________________ ______________________________ ______________________________	

CHAPTER(S) ________	Starting page number ______
Make a bullet point list as you read.	Draw a picture of your favorite part.
________________ ________________ ________________ ________________ ________________ ________________ ________________	

CHAPTER(S) ________	Starting page number ______
________________ ________________ ________________ ________________ ________________ ________________ ________________	

CHAPTER(S) ________	Starting page number ______
Make a bullet point list as you read.	Draw a picture of your favorite part.

CHAPTER(S) ________	Starting page number ______

CHAPTER(S) ________ Make a bullet point list as you read.	Starting page number ______ Draw a picture of your favorite part.
______________________________ ______________________________ ______________________________ ______________________________ ______________________________ ______________________________ ______________________________	
CHAPTER(S) ________	Starting page number ______
______________________________ ______________________________ ______________________________ ______________________________ ______________________________ ______________________________ ______________________________	

CHAPTER(S) ________ Make a bullet point list as you read.	Starting page number _______ Draw a picture of your favorite part.
___ ___ ___ ___ ___ ___ ___	
CHAPTER(S) ________	Starting page number _______
___ ___ ___ ___ ___ ___ ___	

WHAT ABOUT IT?

My rating	☆ ☆ ☆ ☆ ☆
What was the theme (message)? What did the author want you to learn?	
What was your favorite part? Explain.	
Did you notice the author using any literary devices? (Literature terms)	
Would you change anything in the book?	
Other notes about the book.	

REFERENCE

DEPTH OF KNOWLEDGE WHEEL (DOK LEVELS)

Challenge your depth of understanding by using words that encourage you to dig deeper. When discussing, try to get past level one to push yourself.

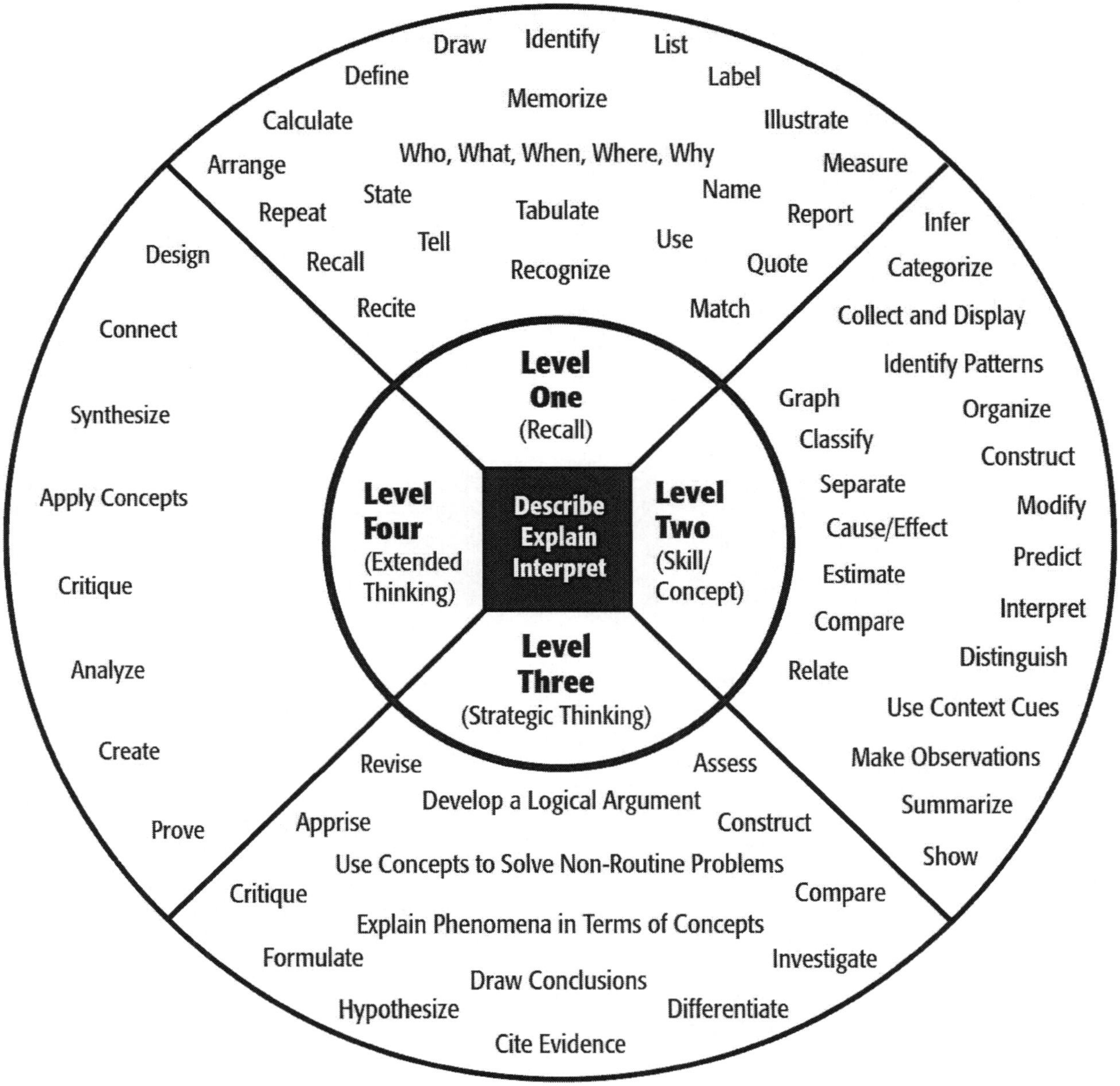

Chart based on Bloom's Taxonomy.

Webb, Norman L. and others. "Web Alignment Tool" 24 July 2005. Wisconsin Center of Educational Research. University of Wisconsin-Madison. 2 Feb. 2006.

ANALYSIS & DISCUSSION WORDS

Definitions	**Remembering**	**Understanding**	**Applying**	**Analyzing**	**Evaluating**	**Creating**
Bloom's Definition	Exhibit memory of previously learned material by recalling facts, terms, basic concepts, and answers.	Demonstrate understanding of facts and ideas by organizing, comparing, translating, interpreting, giving descriptions, and stating main ideas.	Solve problems to new situations by applying acquired knowledge, facts, techniques, and rules in a different way.	Examine and break information into parts by identifying motives or causes. Make inferences, and find evidence to support generalizations.	Present and defend opinions by making judgments about information, validity of ideas, or quality of work based on a set of criteria.	Compile information together in a different way by combining elements in a new pattern or proposing alternative solutions.
Verbs & Actions	Choose Define Find How Label List Match Name Omit Recall Relate Select Show Spell Tell What When Where Which Who Why	Classify Compare Contrast Demonstrate Explain Extend Illustrate Infer Interpret Outline Relate Rephrase Show Summarize Translate	Apply Build Choose Construct Develop Experiment with Identify Interview Make use of Model Organize Plan Select Solve Utilize	Analyze Assume Categorize Classify Compare Conclusion (of) Contrast Discover Dissect Distinguish Divide Examine Function Inference (from) Inspect List Motivation of Relationship (between) Simplify Survey Take part in Test for Theme	Agree Appraise Assess Award Choose Compare Conclude Criticize Decide Deduct Defend Determine Disprove Estimate Evaluate Explain Influence of Interpret Judge Justify Mark Measure Opinion Perceive Prioritize Prove Rate Recommend Rule on Support Value	Adapt Build Change Choose Combine Compile Compose Construct Create Delete Design Develop Discuss Elaborate Estimate Formulate Imagine Improve Invent Make up Maximize Minimize Modify Originate Plan Predict Propose Solve Suppose Test Theorize

Bloom's Revised Taxonomy. Anderson, L. W., & Krathwohl, D. R. (2001). A taxonomy for learning, teaching, and assessing, Abridged Edition. Boston, MA: Allyn and Bacon.

DISCUSSION QUESTIONS FOR FICTION

1. How did this book make you *feel*?
   Happy, intrigued, amused, upset, bored, anxious?
   Was it hard to get through? Or hard to put down?
   Do you feel satisfied? Or are there unresolved (unanswered) feelings?

2. How did you like the way the story was told?
   How was the pacing? Was is too fast, too slow, or just right?
   Was it told in order (chronological/linear) or were there flashbacks (non-linear)?

4. How did you connect to the characters in the novel?
   Did you like the characters? Did you dislike any?
   Did you like the perspective from which it was told?
   Were the characters dynamic (they changed) or static (they stayed the same)?
   Were the characters believable? Or did you think "no way they would do that?"
   Are they fully developed as complex human beings like real peoples? Or were they one-dimensional (only acted one way)?
   Did you think the characters made good decisions? Or poor decisions?
   What motivated the main character to do things?
   Would you like to meet any of the characters? Why?

5. What was the setting of the novel like?
   Did the setting make the book better or worse?
   Could you imagine living in that world?

6. What was your favorite part?
   Do you have a favorite quote? Why does it speak to you?
   What did you relate to in the novel?

7. Was there a main theme?
   Was there a moral or lesson that was being taught?
   What points do you think the author was trying to make (or teach)?
   Did you learn anything you can apply to your own life?

8. Did you notice any symbolism in the novel? What was it? Explain.
   A dove is a symbol of peace and red roses a symbol of love. What did the author use in the book? Did the symbol add meaning to the book?

9. What was unique (original) about this book?
10. If you could give the book another title, what would it be?
11. How can you apply this book to your life?

DISCUSSION QUESTIONS FOR NON-FICTION

1. What was the main idea discussed in the book?
2. Do the issues in the book impact your life? Or someone you know? Explain.
3. What was your favorite part of the book?
4. How is the culture shown in the book different from your own?
5. Did you learn something new?
6. Did the book change your perspective on something?
   An event? A culture?
7. What does the book say about family, politics, or faith (belief or religion)?
8. Are there any quotes that you were drawn to?
9. What type of facts are presented?
10. What information can you apply to your life after reading this book?
11. How does this book impact the future?
12. Is the topic controversial (can cause arguments)?
    If so, how? And how do you feel about the topic?
13. Is the book biased (showing unfair support)?
    Are they coming from a particular point of view?
    Or are they neutral and just trying to get information to the reader?
14. What does the author say about culture?
    Do they want to change it?
    Celebrate it? Criticize it?
    Create a legacy?
15. If the book presents a problem, did it present any solutions?
    Do you have any ideas for a solution? Explain.
16. Why is it important to look back at this event?
    Is our society in danger of repeating the same mistake?
    Or, are specific people supposed to learn something?
17. Is there a call to action?
    In other words, does the book try to convince you to do something?
    Is the action achievable?
18. Can you sum up the message in one sentence?
    Or one paragraph?

PLOT DIAGRAM

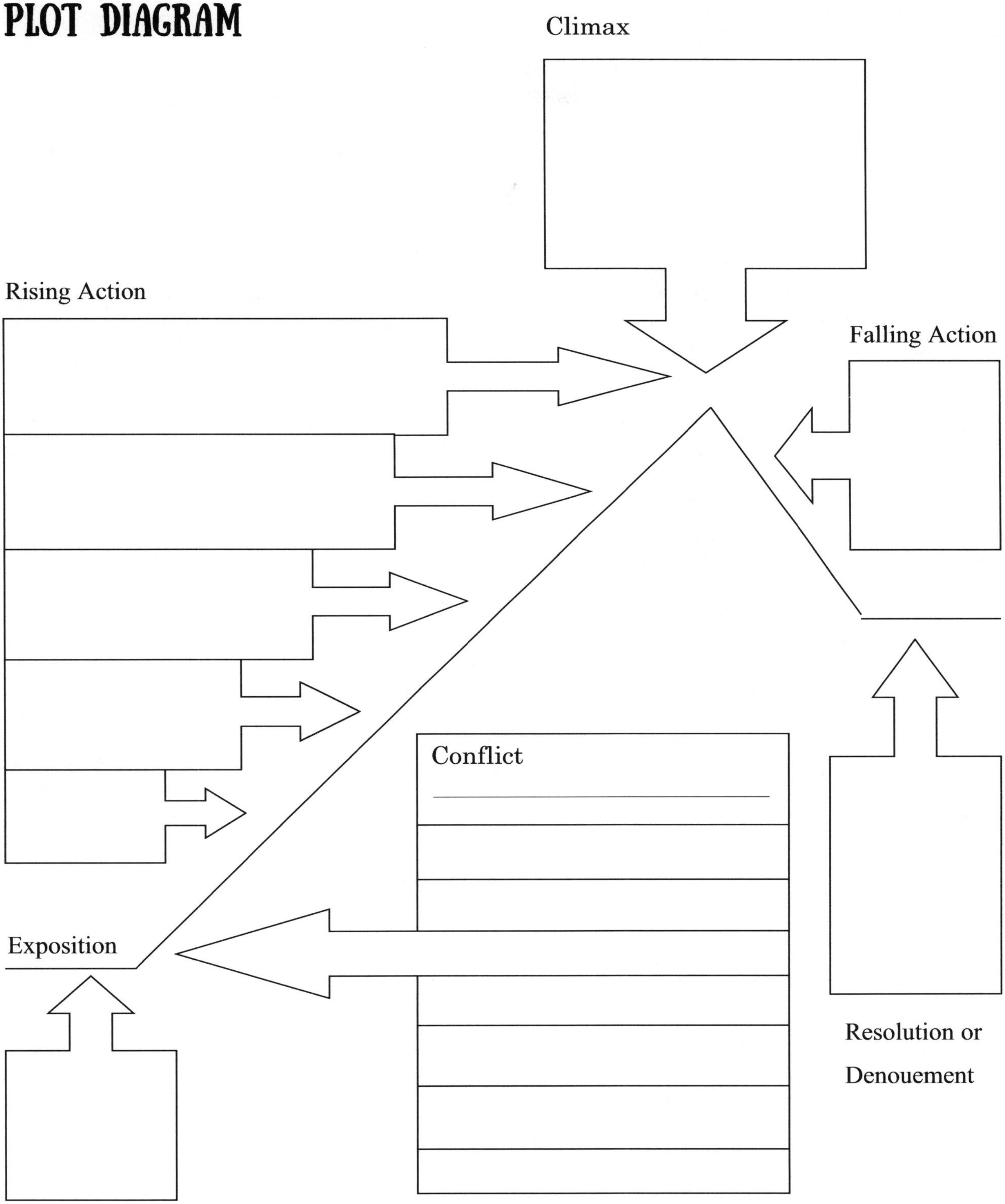

CREATIVE PROJECTS

ARTSY

- If one of the characters kept a scrapbook of things that were important to him or her, what would be in it? Draw one or two pages of the scrapbook (include a minimum of five items).
- Draw a map of the book. Include all the important physical locations and symbols. Please have a clear title and a legend explaining the scale.
- Draw a picture of a character in the novel. Include historical detail and use as many details from the book description as possible. Does the character represent something symbolically? Is there a location where the character always goes? Do they have a favorite piece of clothing or jewelry?
- Recreate your favorite scene in the novel by either making a poster or a comic. If you choose a comic, include important dialogue.
- Make a diorama of the setting.
- Create a board game using the book.
- Make a video about the book. Reenact a scene, create a movie trailer, or conduct a television-style interview with a character.
- Research and cook food from the time period.
- Create a playlist of music that represents the book or a character in it.
- Make a timeline of events and decorate it.
- Assemble a magazine collage of theme, symbols, or characters.

WRITING

- If you could insert yourself as a character in the novel, who would you be? Write a key scene where your character gets to take part.
- Write a poem from the perspective of one of the characters. Try to choose words the character would use.
- Rewrite a scene from a different character's perspective. What would that character have seen that the narrator wouldn't have?
- Interview one of the characters. You can be the interviewer or have two characters interview one another.
- Write a script for your favorite scene. Include costume and prop notes.
- Rewrite the end of the book. Try to change it in an unexpected way.

ANNOTATIONS

If you would like to challenge yourself, try marking the following items in your book. Underline the text, and use the code in the margin to quickly identify the element.

Author & Author's Craft

Abbreviations for Literary Elements

- A = Alliteration
- AL = Allusion
- Con = Conflict (Internal/External)
- Fig = Figurative Language
- F = Foreshadowing
- H = Hyperbole
- Hum = Humor
- I = Imagery
- IR= Irony
- M= Metaphor
- PS = Parallel Structure
- P = Plot
- PER = Personification
- Sim = Simile
- S = Setting
- SD = Sound Device (assonance, repetition, etc.)
- Sym = Symbol
- TH = Theme
- T = Tone (or mood)
- U = Understatement

Abbreviations for Characterization

- C = Characterization
- CD = Character Description
- Direct Characterization using Narrative = DCN
- Direct Characterization using Dialogue = DCD
- Indirect Characterization = IC

- Point out the use of literary techniques and how they add meaning to the text.
- What does the AUTHOR want me to know?
- What does the AUTHOR want me to think? (Perspective)
- What does the AUTHOR want me to feel, and how does the AUTHOR do this?

WORDS THAT MAKE YOU A BETTER READER

Adversary	Someone who works in opposition (against)
Aplomb	Stays cool and composed under pressure
Apprehensive	Worry about possible evil or harm
Aptitude	Natural ability
Attentive	Taking notice of something
Banish	Send away from a place of residence, as for punishment
Barricade	Block off with barriers (walls, fences, or piles of junk)
Bluff	Frighten someone by pretending to be stronger than one is
Brackish	Slightly salty (often said about water)
Brandish	Move or swing back and forth (like swinging a sword)
Circumference	The distance around something (usually a circle)
Commotion	Uproar of noise movement
Concoction	Any food dish made by combining different ingredients
Conspicuous	Obvious to the eye or mind
Contortion	A tortuous and twisted shape or position
Cunning	Shrewdness as demonstrated by being skilled in deception
Debris	The remains of something that has been destroyed
Defiance	A hostile challenge
Deft	Skillful in physical movements, especially of the hands
Diminish	Decrease in size, extent, or range
Disdain	Lack of respect accompanied by a feeling of intense dislike